Mimi Vang Olsen
CATS
COLORING BOOK

Artist Mimi Vang Olsen travels the world, meeting with cats and gathering the information she needs to create her colorful and folksy pet portraits. Vang Olsen always incorporates something from the cat's home setting into the portrait—maybe a favorite sofa, a garden sanctuary, or a treasured toy—to show what makes that cat happy. Through careful observation, she is able to capture the unique personality of her feline subject in paint. If there's more than one cat in the household, she often paints them together as a family.

You'll find twenty-two of Vang Olsen's cat portraits in this coloring book. They are shown as small reproductions on the inside front and back covers. When you color in the pictures, you might want to copy the colors the artist used, or you might be inspired to use different ones.

Mimi Vang Olsen painted her first portrait of her black-and-white cat, Coody, when she was twelve years old. We've left the last page of this book blank so that you can draw and color a picture of your own cat or other favorite pet. Think about your pet's favorite sunny spot or toy, and add that to your picture.

Pomegranate

Many of the images in this coloring book are details of the original artwork. Paintings included are of the following splendid cats:

1. Pru
2. Muammar
3. Pau and Silenci
4. Shepsut
5. Mützu
6. Onyx
7. Chaplin, Roxy, and Fats
8. Goldie
9. Petra and Smocker
10. Eli
11. Otto and His Mother
12. Minette
13. Hudson, Charles, and Daniel
14. White Nose and Toto
15. Augie
16. Mussie
17. Maggie
18. Kipples and Ginger
19. Emma
20. Poppi
21. Momma, Poppa, and Baby
22. Chips

Pomegranate Communications, Inc.
19018 NE Portal Way, Portland OR 97230
800 227 1428   www.pomegranate.com

Color reproductions © 2011 Mimi Vang Olsen
Line drawings © Pomegranate Communications, Inc.

Item No. CB137
Designed and rendered by Susan Koop
Printed in Korea
24 23 22 21 20 19 18 17 16 15   13 12 11 10 9 8 7 6 5 4

Distributed by Pomegranate Europe Ltd.
Unit 1, Heathcote Business Centre, Hurlbutt Road
Warwick, Warwickshire CV34 6TD, UK
[+44] 0 1926 430111
sales@pomeurope.co.uk

1. Pru

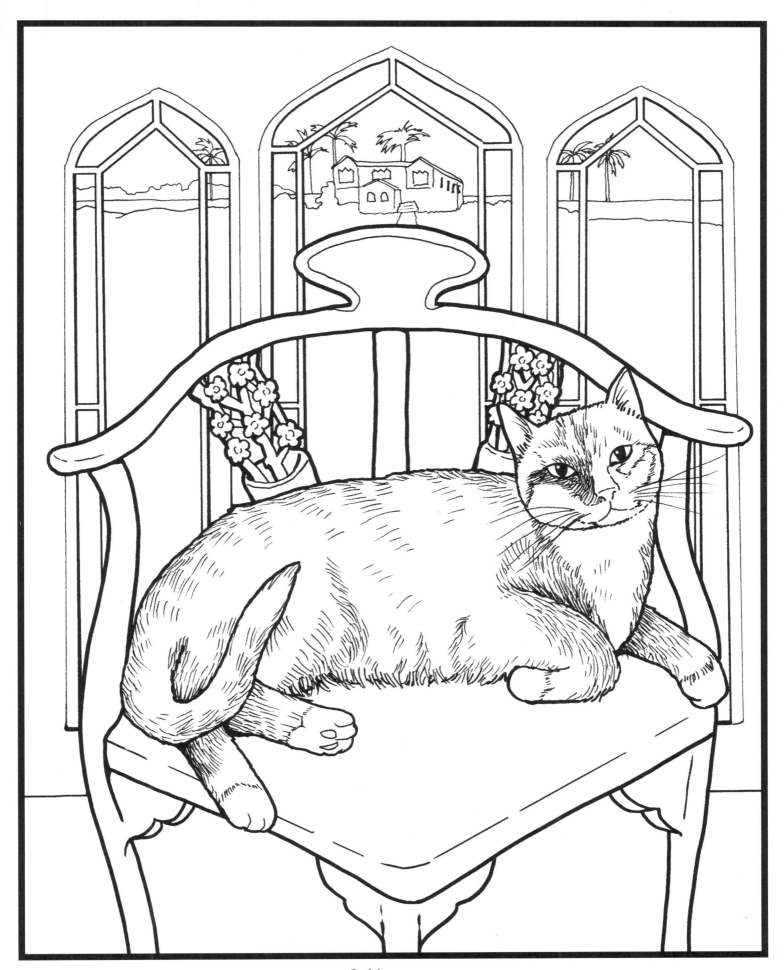

2. Muammar

3. Pau and Silenci

4. Shepsut

5. Mützu

6. Onyx

7. Chaplin, Roxy, and Fats

8. Goldie

9. Petra and Smocker

10. Eli

11. Otto and His Mother

12. Minette

13. Hudson, Charles, and Daniel

14. White Nose and Toto

15. Augie

16. Mussie

17. Maggie

18. Kipples and Ginger

19. Emma

20. Poppi

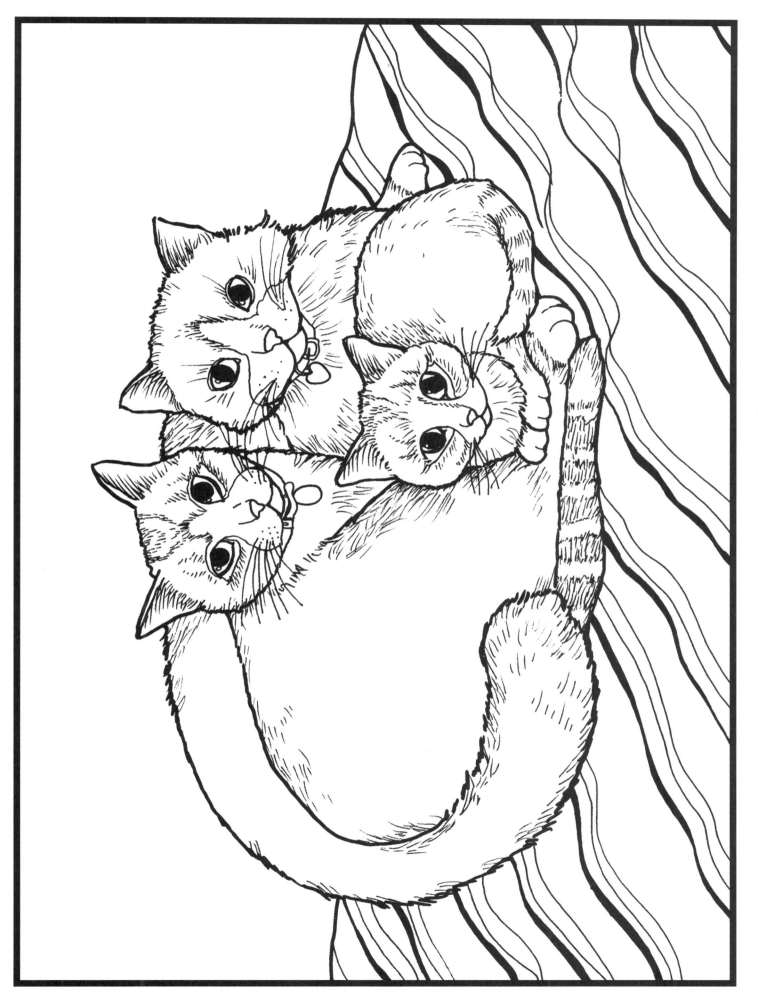

21. Momma, Poppa, and Baby

22. Chips

Draw and color your own picture here!